# Jet Liners

# Jet Liners

*Chris McAllister*

**B T Batsford Ltd**, London

*To my many friends in civil aviation*

## By the same author

*Aircraft Alive –*
*aviation and air traffic for enthusiasts*
Batsford, 1980

*Planes and Airports*
Batsford, 1981

ISBN 0 7134 4162 3

Filmset by Servis Filmsetting Ltd, Manchester
and printed in Hong Kong
for the publishers B T Batsford Ltd,
4 Fitzhardinge Street, London W1H 0AH

*Frontispiece* The wing of the Airbus A300 (*Airbus Industrie*)

## Acknowledgment

I would like to thank all those many
companies and people who helped me in
the writing of this book; those who
provided information, photographs, advice,
travel or photographic facilities, in
particular the following.

Aer Lingus Teoranta, Aerospatiale, Aer
Rianta Irish Airports, Airbus Industrie,
Air France, Airmotive Ireland, British
Aerospace Hatfield-Chester Division,
British Airways, British Caledonian
Airways Limited, British Midland
Airways, Dan-Air Services Limited,
Fokker B.V., Manchester International
Airport Authority, NLM Cityhopper, Orion
Airways Limited.

*Chris McAllister*

# Contents

# Boeings and Bus Stops

The aeroplane's most important peacetime role will always be that of carrying passengers. Flying not only puts any part of the globe speedily within man's reach by reducing much of the delay and tedium of surface transport, but as with any improved means of travel, flying is habit-forming. Like the motor-car, the airliner is here to stay, fuel crises or not. The modern world has grown up with the airliner and become dependent on it. Today's passenger jet is more than just a marvel of technology; it is also a social happening like the cathedrals of the Middle Ages or the railways of the last century. The jetliner has become one of the most powerful symbols of our age.

Flying is no longer just for the privileged few, the rich and the famous, nor even for the businessman dashing between appointments at his firm's expense. Millions of ordinary people use jetliners to visit their friends and relatives or to get to their annual holiday in the sun, and in the developing regions of the world, flying is often the only practicable means of public transport. Buying and operating aircraft, even jet aircraft, may cost less than building roads and railways, and the people of rural villages travel about by air as readily as some hop on a bus.

An airliner as modern as the British Aerospace 146 or the Airbus A310 is the end result of a steady and painstaking process of development. The first real jetliner, Britain's De Havilland Comet 1, went into service in 1952. The Comet was smallish, noisy, thirsty and had a short range compared with most of today's jets. But it set standards of speed and comfort which today's airline passengers take for granted as they are transported to their destinations at around 500mph, high above most of the weather and turbulence. Since the days of the Comet, jetliners have become bigger, quieter, and above all, more economical to operate.

Until the first jet aircraft flew in the late 1930s and early 1940s, the piston-driven, petrol-burning, propeller-turning aero engine, usually air- or oil-cooled, was the only practicable means of getting a powered aeroplane into the sky. Engines such as the Rolls Royce Merlin which powered the Spitfire, Lancaster and Mosquito, or the Pratt and Whitney Twin Wasp which powered the Dakota, were beautiful pieces of machinery, but they were heavy, complicated, temperamental and difficult to maintain. They were full of highly stressed parts which clattered to-and-fro, prone to wear and failure. There were problems with lubrication, problems with cooling and the vibration produced by these big multi-cylindered engines was wearying on the crew and passengers alike. Furthermore, their performance was limited. The higher they flew the less efficient the engines became, and the faster they flew the less efficient the propellers became. 300mph at 25,000 feet was about the limit for the most advanced types of piston-engined airliner of early 1950s vintage. The new jet engines were not only simpler and vibration-

The jetliner is one of the symbols of the age (*PAN AM*).

free, but by a strange contrast their performance and efficiency *improved* the higher and faster they flew. The Comet I could fly as high as 40,000 feet and its speed, close to 500mph, made nonsense of existing airline timetables.

Like a piston engine, a jet engine works by sucking in air, compressing it, mixing it with fuel and burning it to produce a powerful charge of hot, high-pressure gas. But there the resemblance ends. Unlike the piston engine which can only work in separate cylinderfuls, the action of a jet engine (more correctly termed a *gas turbine* engine) is continuous. A rotating compressor sucks in air at the front of the engine and compresses it several times. This high-pressure air is then mixed with fuel and ignited to produce a continuous stream of hot, high-pressure gas. It is the high pressure inside the engine and

exhausting out the rear which pushes the plane forward, and some of the power of the exhaust is used to drive a turbine which is linked to the rotating compressor. Cooling can be arranged easily and both the turbine and the compressor are at opposite ends of a simple rotating shaft mounted on sealed bearings. There are few moving parts, lubrication is easy and there is little or no vibration.

Tragically, Britain's early lead in jetliner technology was shortlived. In 1954 Comets began exploding in mid-air and the type was grounded. Eventually the fault was traced to a failure of part of the pressure cabin as a result of metal fatigue. It took over four years to produce the redesigned Comet IV which was not only stronger but much bigger and heavier, with more powerful engines and greatly improved range. The Comet IV was

*Above opposite* The turbojet-powered Boeing 367-80, prototype of the 707 (*Boeing*).

*Below opposite* The Boeing 720B (*Pakistan International*).

A Boeing 707-320 (*British Caledonian Airways*).

9

the truly great aeroplanes of all time. It began life in 1954 as the Boeing Model 367-80, a prototype built to a military specification, and a civil version, the Boeing 707-120 first flew in 1957. By late 1958 it was in service with Pan American, challenging the Comet IV on the North Atlantic route. The new American plane was much bigger than the Comet and could seat six passengers abreast in its roomy cabin, but this was only the beginning of the 707 story. As more powerful and more fuel-efficient engines became available, the 707 could be developed to carry even more passengers over even longer distances. By the time production of the Boeing 707 ended in the late seventies a total of 962 aeroplanes of all versions had been sold world-wide. This total includes the shorter Boeing 720, but does not include the several hundred extra planes which were built for a variety of military purposes, such as the C-135 transport, the KC-135 flight refuelling tanker, and the E-3A AWACS flying radar station.

The early jet engines worked on what is called the 'turbojet' principle, whereby all the air sucked in at the front is eventually heated before it comes out of the rear. In the late 1950s a new idea was tried, the 'turbofan', 'fan-jet' or 'by-pass' principle. In these jet engines the front end of the compressor takes the form of a huge ducted fan which pushes a lot of air backwards, but only some of this air goes through the hot part of the engine; the rest is by-passed around the engine to mix with the exhaust flow behind. In theory these engines are more economical at typical jetliner speeds than those working on the pure turbojet principle, and so it proved in practice. When turbofan engines were fitted to the early Boeing 707s, the range and fuel economy were greatly improved. The Comet IV, with its four turbojet engines buried in the wing roots, did not have the space to take the fatter turbofans, so the

*Above* A Super 63, one of the 'stretched' versions of the DC-8. This pencil-slim jetliner can carry 259 passengers (*KLM*).

*Below* The rare Convair CV-990A Coronado, showing the unique bulges behind the wing (*Spantax SA*).

able to inaugurate the first transatlantic jet service in October 1958, but by then the Comet was not the only jetliner in the skies. It had been joined by the Russian Tu-104 and the trend-setting rear-engined French Caravelle, while across the water the Americans were getting in on the act with the Boeing 707, the Douglas DC-8 and the Convair 880 and 990.

The Boeing 707 will probably be remembered as *the* classic jetliner and as one of

Aerospatiale Super
Caravelle (*Finnair*).

BAC One-Eleven,
Britain's most
successful jetliner to
date (*Aer Lingus
Teoranta*).

Britain's long-range
four-jet, the VC-10
(*G. Speed*).

Of similar appearance
is the Soviet long-range
four-jet, the Ilyushin
Il-62M, seen here
during a refuelling stop
at Shannon (*Aer
Rianta-Irish Airports*).

British state airline BOAC was forced to buy Boeings instead. Some national pride was salvaged, however; BOAC's Boeing 707s were powered by Rolls-Royce-built Conway turbofans.

The final definitive version of the Boeing 707 was the Model 320, and more of this version were built than of any other. You are likely to see quite a few around. Boeing 707-320s are operated in the UK by British Airways, British Caledonian, Monarch, Tradewinds and British Midlands, and the 320s operated by other airlines are still going strong. It is a stretched version of the earlier 707–120, being some $4\frac{1}{2}$ metres longer and some 35 tonnes heavier, with much more powerful engines. The data given below refers to the Boeing 707-320C which can be used for passengers, cargo, or a mixture of both.

## Boeing 707-320C: facts and figures

*Length* 46.6m, *Span* 44.4m, *Height* 12.9m.
*Accommodation* up to 219 passengers in a cabin 3.6m wide.
*Empty weight* 62–66 tonnes, *Cargo payload* 38 tonnes.
*Maximum take-off weight* 151 tonnes.
*Fuel capacity* 90,377 litres (72 tonnes).
*Power* four Pratt and Whitney JT3D-7 turbofans, each with a take-off thrust of 19,000lb (8.6 tonnes).
*Range with maximum payload* 4300 statute miles.
*Range with maximum fuel* 7475 statute miles.
*Typical long-range cruising speed (35,000 feet)* 532mph (this is the same as 856kmh, 462 knots or Mach 0.81).

It is a pity that aviation today still uses a confusing mixture of imperial, metric and nautical measures, but even so, if we study these figures we can learn a lot, not just about the Boeing 707, but about jetliners generally. For one thing, there is space to carry an enormous amount of fuel, but no plane can take off carrying both maximum fuel *and* maximum payload, so the pilot has to do his weight calculations carefully before the flight, and if necessary, trade off fuel against payload or vice-versa, depending on how far he has to go. However, if we estimate as the airlines do, that each passenger weighs on average 100 kilos, including his baggage, a full complement of 219 passengers will still leave room for some general cargo, again depending on how far it is to the plane's destination or to its next refuelling stop. London to New York is a mere 3456 miles.

The thrust produced by the engines at take-off is a good 34 tonnes, but at 35,000 feet where the air is thinner this is reduced to a bare 10 tonnes of thrust. It is staggering to think that these 10 tonnes are keeping 151 tonnes of aeroplane in the sky! The secret, of course, is the wing. It is the wings and not the engines which produce the lift to balance out the weight of the aircraft, passengers, cargo and remaining fuel. The engines merely push the plane through the air, and the air flowing backwards over the specially shaped surfaces of the wing produce the lift. Most of the lift is produced by the upper surface of the wing in the form of suction, caused by the speeding up of the air as it passes.

The sound to which our ears are attuned consists of pressure waves, and at sea level under typical conditions these pressure waves travel through the air at a speed of 762mph. In the colder air at 35,000 feet the speed of pressure waves, sound, or Mach One as it is called, is reduced to around 660mph. Although most jetliners (Concorde and Soviet Tu-144 excepted) have a maximum speed which is below this, the air being speeded-up over the top surface of the wing may reach Mach One under certain

A Hawker Siddeley Trident 2 (*a British Airways photograph*).

The world best-selling Boeing 727 medium-range tri-jet. Compare the tail and fin with that of the Tu-154 in the background and the Trident (above).

conditions, producing shock waves and dangerous buffeting. It is to prevent this happening that the wings, tail, etc., of a jetliner have to be swept back; in the case of the 707 by as much as 40 degrees.

Two other big four-engined long-range jetliners appeared in the USA at about the same time as the Boeing 707. The Douglas DC-8 also had a successful career, with over 500 built and sold by the time it went out of production in 1972. There are lots of DC-8s left flying and many of these are the later 'superstretched' versions such as the DC-8 Super 61 and Super 63 with accommodation for as many as 259 passengers in their long, pencil-slim cabins. The Convair, on the other hand, is now a rarity. The Madrid-based charter airline Spantax still operates 11 Convair CV-990A Coronados, a unique aeroplane in that the wings have four large carrot-shaped bulges sticking out above and behind the trailing edge. These bulges are there to assist the airflow at high Mach numbers and are not to be confused with the flap-track fairing bulges fitted *below* the wings on many other types of aircraft.

The early 1960s were a boom period for producing new types of jetliner, almost all of which followed the trend started by the Caravelle of having rear-mounted engines and a high tailplane. Two of the new designs were long-range jetliners comparable in performance to the 707, with four rear-mounted turbofans; Britain's VC-10 and the similar (but larger) Soviet-designed Ilyushin Il-62. The VC-10 was powered by four Rolls Royce Conway turbofans and was designed specifically for BOAC, who needed a long-range jetliner capable of using short runways in the 'hot and high' conditions of many of the company's African and Far Eastern staging posts. The VC-10 had a very distinguished career with BOAC/British Airways, and was very popular with passengers; however, it

did not sell well abroad and in the end only 54 were built, including 14 for the RAF, which now remains the only large operator of the VC-10.

The other jetliners produced at this time were all intended for short and medium ranges. Airlines everywhere were re-equipping with jets, and a huge market was

*Above* Tupolev 134A, with a glazed nose for use by a tactical observer/navigator.

*Below* The 158-seater Tupolev Tu-154B. Note the six-wheel main undercarriage.

The Fokker F-28
Fellowship is a small
but very successful
jetliner operating into a
number of British
airports (*NLM
Cityhopper*).

McDonnell-Douglas
DC-9-15, one of several
in the livery of British
Midland Airways.

opening up, with a clear need for planes
specially designed for short hops and quick
turnrounds – in other words 'Bus-Stop Jets'.
All these new planes had rugged undercarriages, their own built-in airstairs, Auxiliary Power Units (APUs) to keep the aircraft's
systems running while on the ground, and
equipment which needed very little maintenance between flights. The new bus-stop jets
were able to land and take off again in as little
as ten minutes if required.

Britain's two medium-range jetliners at
this time were the Trident and the BAC One-
Eleven, both powered by the Rolls Royce
Spey turbofan. With three rear-mounted
Speys, the Trident was first in the air, and a
large number were sold to BEA (later to be
part of British Airways) and to the People's
Republic of China. But it was the One-
Eleven which was the big export success.
The first order was placed by Freddie Laker
for his Gatwick-based airline British United,

and a total of over 200 BAC One-Elevens were sold altogether, most of them going abroad. They are still being built under licence in Romania. Another aircraft which is powered by two rear-mounted Speys is Holland's beautiful little go-anywhere Fokker F-28 Fellowship.

Meanwhile, back across the Atlantic, Boeing was building up to a world sales record with their 727 medium-range jetliner, powered by three rear-mounted JT8D turbofans but using the same fuselage cross-section and nose as the 707. Total world sales of all versions of the Boeing 727 medium-range bus-stop jetliner now stand at over 1800 and the type has been in continuous production for over 20 years. The McDonnell Douglas DC-9 is another American bus-stop jet whose sales have reached four figures, and is powered by two rear-mounted JT8DS.

The JT8D turbofan is clearly Pratt and Whitney's answer to the Rolls Royce Spey, and has also been chosen by the French to power the Super Caravelle, a stretched version of the original trend-setting design, and the Dassault Breguet Mercure, ordered so far

only by the French domestic airline Air Inter.

Soviet-built jetliners are used in large numbers not only by Aeroflot, the world's largest airline, but also by the national airlines of the USSR's client states throughout the world. Commonest visitors to Western Europe are the long-range four-engined Ilyushin Il-62 and Il-62M (often called the VC-10ski) and the two medium-range Tupolevs, the Tu-134 and Tu-154. The Tu-134 is powered by two rear-mounted turbofans and some of them still have glazed noses because they were designed to double-up as tactical transports for the Warsaw Pact forces. The Tu-154 has three engines and is a large, handsome jetliner which compares well with the Boeing 727 or the British Trident 3. Both Tupolevs have large multi-wheeled heavy-duty undercarriages capable of operating from unpaved runways, and their bulky wheel assemblies retract rearwards into streamlined bulges behind the wings. A novel feature of many Russian airliners is a wardrobe where passengers can hang their bulky winter coats and, one imagines, their fur hats.

Boeing 737-200. The holiday jet (*Orion Airways Limited*).

17

# Happy Holidays

Picture the scene at a regional airport somewhere in Britain during what is supposed to be July. Washed by the early-morning rain, a Boeing 737 which will take 130 inclusive-tour passengers on holiday to Spain stands on the cold windy apron. The captain and first officer are going through the pre-flight checks together. The APU turbine is running, so there is power in the aircraft's systems, and the cabin already feels warm and comfortable as the four stewardesses shepherd the first of the 130 passengers on board. The somewhat-fraught atmosphere of the airport's departure lounges, with their last-minute scramble, passport and security checks, vanishes as the passengers settle themselves in their seats. Their holiday has begun.

The current recession is mostly bad for the airline industry. On the scheduled inter-city routes which used to be thronged with businessmen, planes are flying half-empty and many airlines are in the red. The good news, however, is that the specialist holiday airlines are not yet affected by the recession and may even be enjoying a bit of a boom. Money may be scarce and people may have cut back on their cigarettes and beer, but they are not yet prepared to forego their annual holiday 'away from it all'; neither will they take the chance of a wet fortnight in Blackpool. Around the coasts of the Mediterranean, sun is almost a certainty and flying is the best way to get there. In fact the flight out and back has come to be part of the holiday, and the customers of Britannia, Laker, Air Europe, Orion and Dan-Air no longer expect to be kept waiting around or to travel in second-hand planes. Punctuality and service are important for a holiday airline, and in practice this means buying and operating new aircraft. Most of them have bought Boeing 737s.

The Boeing 737 first flew in 1967. Even so, it was a late starter in the twin-jet market previously dominated by the BAC 1-11, DC-9 and Super Caravelle. For their 100-plus seater short-to-medium range twinjet Boeing retained the six-abreast fuselage cross-section and nose previously used on the 707 and 727, but abandoned the rear-engined T-tailed layout of the 727 and went back to slinging the engines under the wings. A stretched version, the 737-200 was soon on offer, and since 1971 all Boeing 737 sales have been of the 'Advanced 200' version, which has a number of aerodynamic, mechanical and system refinements. Sales were always healthy, but they began to enjoy a boom in the late 1970s, when airlines, worried by rising operating costs, began to realise that the Boeing 737 was one of the most economical ways of getting 130 people to a destination roughly 1000 miles away. Put another way, the 737's operating costs per seat/mile are lower than that of any other jetliner in its size bracket, making it the obvious choice for the holiday airlines, provided they can fill it. Sir Freddie Laker's DC-10s and Airbus A300s are even bigger and

*Opposite* A Dan-Air stewardess welcomes passengers aboard a BAC One-Eleven.

cheaper to operate per seat/mile, but then his agents have to sell a lot more holidays.

The chances are that if you have flown at all, you have been on a 737 at some time or another, and it is equally probable that for many people their first experience of jet flying will be aboard the comfortable, efficient and economical Boeing 737 – the holiday jet.

Our plane today is a Boeing 737-2T5 bought brand-new from Boeing only last year, powered by a pair of Pratt and Whitney JT8D-9As, has a flight crew of two and four stewardesses, with seats for 130 passengers and their baggage. Cargo is not usually carried on flights to holiday destinations, but there is a fair weight of catering stores and duty-free goods aboard.

## Boeing 737-200 Advanced: facts and figures

*Length* 30.5m, *Wingspan* 28.4m,
  *Height* 11.3m.
*Wing sweepback* 25 degrees.
*Accommodation* up to 130 passengers at
  31-inch seat pitch six abreast. *Cabin
  width* 3.7m.
*Maximum take-off weight* 52.6 tonnes,
  *Cargo payload* 16 tonnes.
*Fuel capacity* 19,530 litres (15.6 tonnes).
*Power* two Pratt and Whitney JT8D-9A
  turbofans each with a take-off thrust of
  14,500lb (6.6 tonnes).
*Range with maximum payload* 2370 miles.
*Range with maximum fuel* 2530 miles.
*Typical economical cruise at 30,000 feet*
  484mph (778kmh, 420 knots or Mach
  0.73).

Already the passengers are seated, the doors are closed, the engines have been started, the cabin staff have done the safety briefing, and the plane is trundling along the concrete towards the runway holding point. The 737

Inclusive-tour passengers boarding a 737 as it is refuelled.

The 737's high performance is demonstrated by this steep climb after take-off (*Boeing*).

*Opposite* In-flight service aboard a Boeing 737 (*Air Europe*).

does not need a long runway on which to land or take off; the elaborate leading-edge slats and slotted Fowler flaps give the wing the ability to lift the plane at quite slow airspeeds. For take-off the slats are fully extended and the flaps are partly extended.

When the airport tower gives take-off clearance, the engines will be run up to full power and the brakes will be released. The plane will roar down the runway until it reaches an airspeed of 144 knots, then the captain will ease the control wheel back slightly. This is

*Above* A Boeing 737-236 seen from below. Notice the long engine pods and the wheels still partly showing (*a British Airways photograph*).

The runway at Ibiza as seen from the flight deck.

*Opposite* The view from on high can be very beautiful. Here a low sun reflects with a coppery sheen from the sea (*British Caledonian Airways*).

when the passengers get a sinking feeling in their stomachs as their plane noses up, leaps into the air, and begins to climb away from the runway at a steep angle, the steepest of the entire flight as the engines continue to deliver full power and fuel is being burnt by each of them at a rate of $1\frac{1}{2}$ litres a second. Once safely up to 1000 feet or so, the throttles will be eased back, power and fuel burn will be reduced (partly as a noise-abatement measure) and the climb will be more gentle.

The wheels have long since been tucked away and the plane has already swung round in a wide banking turn towards the south.

The pilot finds his way to Spain along the standard airways which are marked out by a network of radio beacons. These define the geography of the air lanes as precisely as marker buoys in a shipping channel, and our route today will take us via the beacons at Midhurst, Chartres, Amboise, Limoges, Gaillac, Barcelona and Palma. Each beacon in turn is tuned on the navigation radio, and the course towards it is set on the autopilot, which steers the plane. Another radio device, the DME (Distance Measuring Equipment) sends a coded signal to the beacon and times the split second which it takes the beacon to reply. This split second is computed by the DME and displayed on the flight deck as the distance to go to the beacon, the speed and the time it will take to get there. Radar scanners on the ground follow our progress and we show up as a numbered blip on the air traffic controllers' radarscopes. The controllers' job is to make sure that the blips keep clear of each other. Soon the controller responsible for our part of the sky gives our pilot clearance to climb to his planned cruising altitude of 33,000 feet. Level at this height, the pilot adjusts the power to give a cruising speed of around Mach 0.73, just under 500mph, which should prove most economical in today's conditions. Soon we are crossing the French coast near Le Havre, and although nothing can be seen because of the cloud, down below is where they all speak French and drive on the 'wrong' side of the road.

'Good Morning. This is the captain speaking. We are just about to cross the French coast near Le Havre, cruising at a speed of 480mph at a height of 33,000 feet. Our route will take us down through the middle of France past Limoges and Toulouse. The weather in Ibiza is fine and sunny and we expect to be landing at about 10.45 local time.'

Flying in one of today's jetliners is such a cossetted experience that it all seems a bit unreal. A fairyland cloudscape slides past the windows while the passengers relax in comfortable seats in the air-conditioned cabin and the stewardesses flit about with food and drinks as we race along at 500mph six miles above the ground. Even at this speed the manoeuvres made by the plane are gentle and

hardly perceptible. Meanwhile, outside the cabin, the environment is hostile and often far from gentle. The towering clouds glowing brilliant white in the sunshine contain violent storms. The 500mph gale outside the cabin windows is 40 degrees below freezing and behind the plane's engines the vapour in the exhaust condenses out into a white trail of millions of tiny ice crystals. The air at 33,000 feet is only a quarter of the density and one-third of the pressure of air at sea level. Most humans would remain conscious only for seconds at this low pressure, so the plane's cabin has to be artifically pressurised using air bled from the engine fans.

In this thin air the wing has to work harder to keep the plane flying, so we cruise along in a slightly nose-up attitude and the stewardesses complain about having to push their trolleys uphill. But there is also less drag and we can fly fast using less fuel per mile; it is one of the everyday facts about jet flying that it pays to fly high. The engines are revving just as fast as they were before, but the weight of air being swallowed is much less than when we were on the ground. We don't need to mix as much fuel with it; fuel burn is only a quarter of what it was on take-off and the thrust is much reduced. On the flight-deck the engine power levers have been pulled back almost as far as the 'idle' setting. It is quieter, too.

The voice of the French air-traffic controller intrudes onto the flight deck; 'Kilo Golf Seven Zero Three. Please maintain three-three-zero direct to Limoges.' The pilot acknowledges and notices as he does so that the cloud below is breaking up. Quite large patches of the French countryside can now be seen, including the city of Tours astride the Loire. He picks up the intercom telephone and points out the city and the river to the passengers.

Back in the cabin the stewardesses have finished clearing away the remains of the

A Boeing 737 dangles its wheels, slats and flaps on the approach to land.

In landing trim, a shiny new Boeing 737 of Orion Airways parades to show off the complex engineering of its flaps, slats, speedbrakes and thrust reversers.

mid-morning snack, and any apprehensions the passengers might have had about flying have long since evaporated. It really is quite a pleasant way to travel. The six-abreast seating with an aisle down the centre is ideal for couples and families, and because few people will be travelling on holiday alone, no-one feels isolated in the middle seat, hemmed in by hefty strangers on either side, as tends to happen on businessmen's flights. Passengers busy themselves talking or reading, or doing the crossword in the in-flight magazine. The orchards and vineyards slip by below and soon we are crossing the Pyrenees into Spain by way of Andorra.

When we get as far as the Spanish coast near Barcelona the captain and his first officer will have begun to think about the landing and to plan the descent. The best way not to waste fuel is to start the descent at the right time, to shut the engines down to flight idle, let the speed fall off slightly, then begin a gentle nose-over into a long, fast, shallow dive in which gravity is doing much of the work. A slope of 300 feet per mile (1 in 20) or a rate of descent of 700 feet per minute, depending on speed, is ideal. But the approach controller may have his own system, especially if the sky is busy, and may ask the captain to descend in a series of awkward steps, which may mean using the power to fly level again one minute, then plummeting steeply down with speedbrakes open a moment later.

The speedbrakes on a 737 are a set of hinged panels on top of the wings, and the passengers can sometimes see these open slightly as the plane goes downhill. There will be some extra noise and a small amount of juddering. In theory, if a pilot is aiming to save fuel, he should be able to descend without using the speedbrakes at all, but in practice, due to the arrangements of air traffic control, this is rarely possible, and it is usual to pull open the speedbrakes when

height and speed have to be got rid of quickly.

Our plane navigates around the Balearics via a set of radio beacons and soon the island of Ibiza is in view with the airport ahead and Formentera stretching away behind it. In bad weather the autopilot could be set to lock onto the beams from the Instrument Landing System (ILS) and fly down these to within sight of Runway 25, but today the weather is clear and sunny and we can land visually from the opposite direction, which will take us in over the sea against the light breeze. We fly south of the airport then turn around to the right to line up for the runway. The wheels go down, the flaps and slats come fully out and the speed drops back to about 150 knots. In order to keep the plane flying at this speed with all its clobber hanging out, the engines rev up again.

Passengers sitting behind the wing on the right get a spectacular view of the runway as the plane turns in towards it on final approach, poised over the sea, with the huge triple-slotted flaps hanging a long way out and down. Flaps and slats (high-lift devices) increase the lifting power of the wing to compensate for the loss in speed as the plane comes in to land. A jet could land without flaps, but at a much higher speed and it would need a lot more runway on which to stop. At about 70 feet above the runway the pilot eases back on the controls to bring the nose up slightly to flatten the landing. Bump. We touch down at 130 knots on a part of the runway already heavily streaked with black tyre-marks.

For the next couple of seconds 'it's all happening', as they say. Almost immediately the speedbrakes on top of the wing spring fully open and the thrust-reversing buckets come out to clang into position behind the jet exhaust. The engines rev up again, but now they are blasting against the buckets, pushing us backwards and slowing us down with

An aircraft which is often compared with the Boeing 737, the French-built, JT8D powered Dassault Breguet Mercure (*Air Inter*).

The world's only three-and-a-half-engined jetliner, the Trident 3, has a small turbojet in the base of the fin to help out its three Rolls Royce Speys.

help from the wheelbrakes. We turn off the runway and trundle along a taxiway towards the terminal where we park and shut down. The doors open and as the passengers dis-embark they are greeted by the warm sun. They collect their baggage, pass quickly through the airport formalities and find a coach waiting to take them to their hotels.

# Stretch, Size and Speed

The airlines want the manufacturers to sell them bigger and better planes, able to carry more passengers and cargo without a big increase in operating costs or the need for expensive retraining. One way to achieve this, at least up to a point, is to take an existing successful jetliner and to *stretch* it using more powerful engines. Thus Boeing progressively developed the original 707-120 into the much longer and heavier 707-320, and the type ended its 20-year production life some 35 tonnes heavier, 4.5 metres longer, with increased wingspan and take-off power increased by 40 per cent compared with the prototype. Increases in power available from the JT8D turbofan over the years have also made it possible for Boeing to stretch the 727 and 737. The engine started out at a modest 6.4 tonnes take-off thrust, but today's improved versions deliver nearly 9 tonnes. The original Boeing 727–100 was stretched by nearly 6 metres to become the Boeing 727–200, with its maximum take-off weight increased from 77 to 95 tonnes and its passenger capacity more than doubled from 94 to 189 seats. The 737 has been stretched more modestly, but the effort here was concentrated on detailed design improvements which give the latest versions of Boeing 737-200 the kind of performance and operating economy per seat/mile which makes the airlines still queue up to buy what is basically a 17-year old design.

Competing in the same market were Britain's Hawker Siddeley Trident and BAC One-Eleven and their engine, the Rolls Royce Spey. But the Spey began life at 4.5 tonnes thrust and never got to more than 5.7 tonnes. Nonetheless, BAC managed to stretch the 89-passenger One-Eleven to become the 500 Series 'Super One-Eleven' with a capacity of 119 passengers, and Hawker Siddeley progressively developed the Trident 1E, 2E and much larger Trident 3. All three variants are still in service with British Airways. Although the Trident 3 can carry up to 179 passengers, it does this with the help of an extra baby turbojet mounted in the tail, delivering 2.4 tonnes thrust on take-off in addition to the three Rolls Royce Speys. It is the only jetliner in the world with three-and-a-half engines!

However, past masters at stretching aeroplanes are McDonnell-Douglas, who introduced a remarkably stretched version of their long-range four-jet DC-8 in 1966. The DC-8 Super 61 and Super 63 Series versions were some 11 metres longer than the original, with corresponding increases in power and maximum weight. These jetliners look like huge flying pencils, and the DC-8 Super 63 with its capacity for up to 259 passengers was the biggest civil airliner in the world when it first appeared. McDonnell-Douglas have stretched their DC-9 short-range twin-jet no less than *four* times! The DC-9 Series 10 was a fairly modest 90-seater. By using progressively more powerful JT8Ds, and lengthening the fuselage and now and then the wings, McDonnell-Douglas introduced in turn the

DC-9 Series 30 (121 passengers), the DC-9 Series 40 (132 passengers), the DC-9 Series 50 (159 passengers), and now their latest, the DC-9 Super 80 with a capacity for 172 passengers and a fuselage which has been extended by no less than 13 metres compared with the early -10 or -20 versions of the DC-9. Of course, there is more to these developments than adding more-powerful engines, stretching the fuselage and strengthening the undercarriage. Advantage has been taken of the latest advances in jetliner technology to produce planes which are also quieter, more economical and have better computers and flight systems.

But the time comes when stretch is not the answer, and it may be better to move on to something which is very much bigger from the outset. Thus in the 1960s the engine manufacturers began to produce very large turbofans, more than twice as large as anything which had been built before. These were originally intended to power large military transports such as the Lockheed C-5A Galaxy, but civil applications were easy to foresee. On 9 February 1969 the huge Boeing 747 jetliner made its first flight. Public reaction was one of amazement that anything quite so big could lift itself into the air, coupled with fears for the noise and pollution which these monsters might be expected to cause. But the fears proved groundless. The huge new turbofans, Pratt and Whitney JT9Ds, which powered the 747 were if anything quieter and cleaner than the engines of much smaller planes. They were also more fuel-efficient. Within a year or two, the 747 was joined in the skies by other large wide-bodied airliners also powered by large turbofan engines. The DC-10 was powered by three General Electric CF6 turbofans, the Lockheed L-1011 Tristar by three Rolls Royce RB-211s and the Airbus A300 by two CF6s.

These three engines represented a major leap forward in jet technology. All of them are powerful enough to produce between 22 and 26 tonnes take-off thrust. They have huge fans, which give them a by-pass ratio of 4 or 5 to 1. This means that only one-fifth or one-sixth of the air they swallow goes through the hot end of the engine to produce the power, the rest is accelerated past the engine by the large fan, which converts 70 per cent of the engine's power into forward thrust. This high by-pass system is very fuel-efficient, and is also clean and quiet.

The definitive version of the Boeing 747 Jumbo in production today is the 747-200. It has the same dimensions as earlier 747s, but has more powerful engines and is certificated for higher take-off weights.

## Boeing 747-200: facts and figures

*Length* 70.7m, *Span* 59.6m,
 *Height* 19.3m.
*Accommodation* up to 490 passengers in
 6m wide cabin plus 25 tonnes freight.
*Empty weight* 164 tonnes.
*Cargo payload* 113 tonnes (747-200F).
*Fuel capacity* 204,300 litres, 163 tonnes.
*Maximum take-off weight* 378 tonnes.
*Power* four Pratt and Whitney JT9D
 or General Electric CF6
 or Rolls-Royce RB-211-524.
*Take-off thrust* up to 54,000lb (24.5
 tonnes) per engine.
*Typical long-range cruise at 35,000 feet*
 589mph (947kmh), 512 knots, Mach
 0.89).
*Range:*
 *maximum fuel* 7.080 miles, *maximum
 passenger payload* 5500 miles, *maximum
 cargo (747-200F)* 3000 miles.
*Total 747 sales* 570 plus.

The only Boeing 747 which is very different from this specification is the 747SP. This is a shorter, lighter, longer-range version spe-

The 189-passenger Boeing 727-200 (*Alitalia*).

cially designed for long, non-stop, low-density routes up to 9500 miles (e.g. New York–Tokyo). It has a short fuselage and large fin compared with other 747s.

The 747, the DC-10, the Tristar and the Airbus introduced a new experience in air travel, the wide-bodied cabin. Passengers seem to prefer the spacious-looking interior of these aircraft, and there are other advantages too. Remember that under the floor is a cargo hold which is nearly as big as the passenger cabin itself, and it pays to use this space. Air cargo is no longer a cinderella; it is big business for most airlines, and the huge 747 is an excellent cargo-carrier. The freighter versions have a tilt-up nose door for straight-in cargo loading, and other versions

can be fitted with a large side door. Cargo is carried on pallets and nets on the main deck and in specially shaped LD3 or LD6 containers below. These containers also fit the other wide-body jets.

The McDonnell-Douglas DC-10 is powered by three General Electric CF6 turbofans. Number Two engine is fitted at the base of the fin with a straight through air intake, and the other engines are slung below the wings. Although the DC-10 comes in three basic versions, differences between them are slight. The DC-10-10 was designed for US domestic routes, and the DC-10-30 and -40 are the long range intercontinental versions, with extra fuel, more powerful engines, longer wings and a fourth undercar-

BAC One-Eleven 416. This popular aeroplane is powered by Rolls Royce Spey turbofans (*Air UK*).

*Opposite* The DC-9 Super 80 is over 40 feet longer than the original McDonnell-Douglas DC-9. Will this be the final stretch? (*McDonnell-Douglas Ltd.*)

The huge Boeing 747 resembles some giant beast emerging from its lair (*Iberia*).

riage leg to support the extra weight on the ground. The DC-10-40 has Pratt and Whitney engines. Sales of all versions to date are 350 plus.

The Lockheed L-1011 Tristar is also a three-engined wide-body and is often compared with the DC-10. All Tristars have Rolls Royce RB-211 turbofans, with the Number Two engine at the end of the fuselage supplied by an S-shaped air intake. The major versions of the Tristar are the -1, -500 and -200 and examples of all three are to be found in British Airways service. The Tristar -1 is

Boeing 747 SP (*Boeing*).

The extra wheel leg of the Series 30 DC-10 shows in this action shot as the big plane rotates for take-off (*British Caledonian Airways*).

the medium-range version, powered by RB-211-22Bs and with the galleys downstairs to create more space on the main passenger deck. The Tristar -200 and -500 are the long-range versions, carrying extra fuel and with the more powerful RB-211-524B engines. The -500 has a lengthened wing for improved fuel-efficiency, and instead of strengthening the structure which would add weight, the additional stresses caused by turbulence are cancelled out by fitting Active Ailerons. These counteract the stresses at the wingtips instead of passing them along the wing.

British Airways is justly proud of its latest Tristars which, with their advanced digital electronics and computerised Flight Management System, are now the most sophisticated aircraft in its fleet. Millions of pounds' worth of fuel have been saved by program-

*Opposite* Boeing 747-200F freighter, powered by Rolls Royce RB-211-524 turbofans (*a British Airways photograph*).

McDonnell-Douglas
DC-10-Series 30 (*British
Caledonian Airways*).

ming the flight management computer for minimum-cost operation. It does this by computing the weather, operating weights, flightplan and other variables to find the most efficient engine settings for each sector of the flight. As it is a 'real-time' system, it can update its own input as the flight progresses, acting as a link between the navigating systems and the autopilot, over which it has immediate and direct authority, and it also operates the throttles.

Then there is the fourth of the wide-bodies, the A300 Airbus, built by a specially formed European consortium (of which British Aerospace is now a full risk-sharing partner) which makes bits of the plane all over Europe and assembles them in the Aerospatiale factory near Toulouse. The A300 is a short-to-medium range wide-body which is powered by two large turbofans. Sales were slow to pick up at first, but now stand at over 200 with advance orders to take the total to over 500. This figure includes

orders for the somewhat smaller Airbus A310, making Airbus the world's busiest builder of wide-bodied jetliners. The system will be turning out eight aircraft per month soon. The secret of the Airbus success is simple; in one word, economy. For short-haul routes, why use three engines (Tristar and DC-10-10) when you can do the job with only two? Two engines are cheaper to run and to maintain than three, and with no third engine in the tail, there is a big saving in structure weight. What it adds up to once again is less fuel used per seat/mile, the biggest single factor in the calculations of most airlines at the present day. But then, this European aeroplane uses American engines, General Electric CF6s or in some cases Pratt and Whitney JT9Ds. Why not Rolls Royce RB-211s? Why did British Airways order Tristars rather than Airbuses? If we want to know, we have to ask the politicians.

Of course, the Concorde is another highly successful joint venture, involving Britain and France, and the politicians did have fun with this one. They haven't finished yet. A questionmark still hangs over the future of this remarkable and beautiful aircraft, the most ambitious flying machine every built. No other aircraft regularly carries 100 passengers at twice the speed of sound for over three hours without refuelling, cruising at between 50,000 and 60,000 feet. There is no doubt that Concorde is technically superb, but it is expensive to operate.

A total of 18 Concordes have been built since 1967. The prototype 001, which first flew on 2 March 1969, is now in honourable retirement at the French Air Museum at Le Bourget, while its British counterpart 002 is on display at the Royal Naval Air Museum at Yeovilton. The pre-production models have similarly become museum pieces, 01 at Duxford and 02 at Orly. The first production Concorde has been returned to Aerospatiale, leaving 13 still in service, six with British Airways and seven with Air France. The early hopes that world-wide supersonic flying might make it possible to circle the globe in just over a day have never been realised. Increasingly governments have banned supersonic flying over land, so that effectively, only the North Atlantic route remains. British Airways can break even on its Concorde operations, but the fares remain high. Concorde is a gas-guzzler designed in the balmy days when jet fuel cost a bob a gallon.

The Concordes are powered by Rolls Royce Olympus 593 turbojets, not turbofans. They are fitted with afterburners to increase power for take-off and for the transition to supersonic flight. On a typical Concorde service from London to New York, the plane will first fly subsonically towards the Bristol Channel, cruising at Mach 0.95 at about 30,000 feet. Then when well out over the sea, the afterburners will be lit again and the aircraft will accelerate through Mach 1, the 'sound barrier' with hardly a tremor. After Mach 1.6 the afterburners will be switched off and the plane will continue to climb to 50,000 feet and to accelerate as far as Mach 2 – something around 1350mph. By

Lockheed L-1011 Tristar 200 (*a British Airways photograph*).

the time it reaches the eastern seaboard of North America some three hours later, Concorde will have climbed to 60,000 feet. Approach and landing are fairly conventional, except that there are no flaps, and the unique ogee-shaped wings can generate the extra lift they need simply by flying nose up at 10 degrees, giving a landing Concorde the appearance of some strange bird of prey. Touchdown airspeed is around 155 knots (175mph).

Cargo-loading operations.

*Above* Nets and pallets (*Fokker b.v.*).

*Left* Containers shaped to fit lower holds (*British Caledonian Airways*).

The Airbus A300 has not only shown that Europe can build big airliners, but also that two engines can do the work of three (*Airbus Industrie*).

Is this sleek bird now an endangered species? (*Air France*).

41

# Structure and Systems

A commentator at a flying display once described a certain large and venerable aeroplane as '45,000 rivets, all flying in formation'. Perhaps rivets on their own are not the most sophisticated way to hold a modern aeroplane together. Glue is better. Parts which are bonded together using epoxy resin or similar adhesives cannot work loose in service, and there are few rivet holes from which cracks can spread. Parts may be bonded cold, or for better results hot, using a large oven called an autoclave. Aircraft which are bonded have clean, smooth outer skins, like the hulls of racing yachts, and performance and fuel-saving are enhanced.

Another method of building an aeroplane with as few rivets as possible is to sculpt it. Complex parts can be milled in one piece from solid billets instead of being built up and fastened together. This was a technique in which Britain led the way, and was used to make the wings of the Vanguard, Trident, VC-10 and now the Airbus family. Huge planks of aluminium alloy are delivered to the British Aerospace factory at Chester. These planks are about 30mm thick to begin with, but when the automatic milling machines have finished with them, they have been sculpted away to little more than 6mm at the outboard end, tapered and scalloped, with stiffeners left protruding in all the right places. Most of the plank ends up as scrap or swarf which is recycled to make more planks. The spars, ribs and stringers are sculpted in the same way, including the hefty Rib No. 5

in which the undercarriage leg pivots, an H-shaped chunk of metal looking as though it escaped from a battleship. This too is sawn and machined in one piece from the solid. All these parts are riveted together in huge jigs to make the wings of the aircraft. Every week two sets of wings come off the production line and are flown in a Super Guppy freighter to the next stage of the Airbus assembly system.

The wings are the most highly stressed parts of an aeroplane's structure. For efficient flight they must be long and narrow, but at the same time light. They have to be strong enough to carry the weight of the plane, its payload and fuel through buffeting and turbulence. The main load-carrying part of the wing is designed as a hollow box which doubles as a fuel tank. Because so much of the plane's weight often consists of fuel, it makes sense to carry this in the wing where it can be supported directly.

The passengers sitting comfortably at 35,000 feet know very well that their lives depend on air being pumped into the cabin at a greater pressure than that outside. They may not realise how big the pressure difference is, nearly 8lb per square inch, nor how strong the cabin walls have to be in order to withstand an outward force equivalent to 5 tonnes on every square metre. The pressure cabin is another highly stressed part of an aircraft's structure, and the best shape for it is the familiar tube, which encloses not only the passenger deck but the baggage and cargo

At the British
Aerospace Chester
factory, an Airbus A310
wing spar is machined
in one piece from a
solid billet (*British
Aerospace*).

A similar one-piece
A310 lower wing skin
panel is lifted into
position in the
assembly jig (*British
Aerospace*).

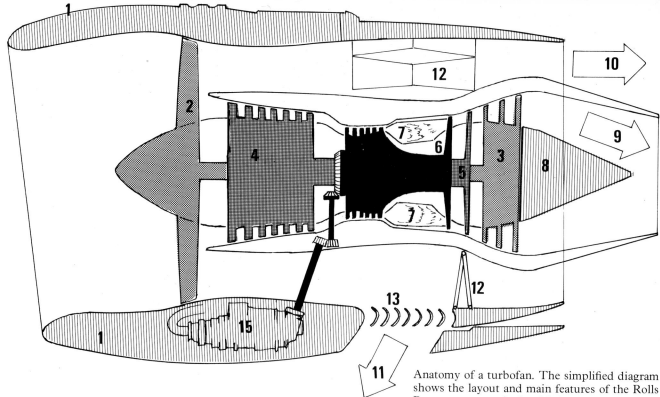

Anatomy of a turbofan. The simplified diagram shows the layout and main features of the Rolls Royce RB-211 turbofan. Notice how the compressor and turbine assemblies are mounted on concentric shafts. The operation of reverse thrust is shown on the lower part of the diagram.

1  Air intake and fan casing with anti-noise linings
2  Fan and hub
3  Three-stage low-pressure turbine driving fan
4  Intermediate compressor
5  Intermediate pressure turbine
6  High-pressure assembly
7  Combustion chamber
8  Tail cone
9  Hot exhaust stream
10  Cold air stream from fan
11  Cold air stream with thrust reversed
12  Thrust-reversing blocker flaps
13  Thrust-reversing cascades
14  Fan casing open for reverse thrust
15  High-speed gearbox

holds as well. In this sealed metal tube, windows and doors are an inconvenience. It is best to have lots of small windows and their spacings may not match that of the rows of seats. Seat spacing is a matter for the customer airline, and a row of seats every 31 inches (31-inch pitch) is now common. Long-legged passengers may tend to feel cramped.

Other parts of the aircraft's structure, such as flaps, slats, nosecones, speedbrakes, undercarriage doors and the like, need to be light yet rigid. They can be made of alloy stiffened with a honeycomb inner structure, or of plastics reinforced with anything from the familiar glassfibre to the much lighter carbon fibre or exotic textiles such as Kevlar.

The RB-211 turbofan delivers nearly 23 tonnes of thrust at take-off. This picture shows two of these giant powerplants on their way through the Derby factory, with their hydraulics, electrics and other plumbing clearly visible on the fan casing (*Rolls Royce Limited*).

Vapour trails or contrails. Under the right
conditions moisture in a jet's exhaust will
freeze to form trails of ice crystals (*a British
Airways photograph*).

On some military aircraft, whole parts of the main structure such as tailfins may be made of reinforced plastics, but jetliners (including the Concordes) are still built mainly of aluminium alloy.

The heart of a jetliner is its engines; those huge open-mouthed monsters which can suck in enormous quantities of air, blast most of it backwards using a large fan, and compress the remainder in gradual stages anything up to 30 times. Then fuel is sprayed into the compressed air and ignited. Inside the combustion chambers of a jet engine the blowtorch flame temperature rises close to 2000°C, and more of the compressed air is immediately added to cool it down. A large

The superbly laid-out flightdeck of the F-28 Fellowship (*Fokker B.V.*).

volume of hot gas is produced, and at a pressure of anything up to 25 atmospheres this rushes out of the engine's tailpipe, spinning the turbines as it passes. Jet engines are violent, noisy machines, but big strides have been made recently in designing engines which are quieter, cleaner and less wasteful of fuel.

Of these modern engines, the Rolls Royce RB-211 turbofan is typical. This huge engine powers the Tristar and some versions of the Boeing 747, generating anything up to 25 tonnes thrust per engine for take-off. But as most of the power is transmitted by means of the huge fan pushing a large volume of air fairly slowly, the RB-211 is much less noisy than the Concorde's turbojet engines which have no large fan, and which transmit all their power via the hot, violent, high-speed jet exhaust. More noise is absorbed by acoustic linings in the fan duct and tailpipe, and careful design of the combustion chamber of the RB-211 ensures that all the fuel is burnt and we are not left with embarrassing trails of black smoke. Great efforts have also been made to improve this engine's fuel efficiency, particularly as measured by specific fuel consumption in the cruise. The RB-211 specific fuel consumption (SFC) of 0.64 means that 0.64 tonnes of fuel are needed to produce a tonne of thrust per hour. Clearly, the lower the SFC, the more fuel-efficient the engine, and the RB-211 is more fuel-efficient than most.

The RB-211 has three separate compressor assemblies, each driven by its own turbine, and with the connecting shafts running inside each other. The outermost arrangement is called the high-pressure spool, and the front end of this spool has a geared drive connecting with a high-speed gearbox in the fan casing. This gearing arrangement drives the fuel pumps, the oil pumps, a generator for electric power, and a hydraulic pump. All of these auxiliary systems are mounted on the

fan casing where they can be got at easily for routine maintenance.

Compressed air for cabin pressurisation and other purposes is simply tapped from the various compressor stages when the engine is running. When the engines are stopped, electric power, hydraulic power and compressed air have to be supplied by plugging into a truck called a Ground Power Unit. Alternatively, jetliners designed since 1960 now carry their own Auxiliary Power Unit (APU) in the form of a small turbine mounted near the tail. The APU can be kept running on the ground and it will keep the aircraft's systems powered up.

A typical procedure for starting a jetliner from cold is to use the plane's 28V DC batteries to start up the APU. This little turbine generates enough power to start the engines, one at a time, by spinning up the high-pressure spool via a starter motor connected to the high-speed gearbox. When a suitable speed is reached, fuel is pumped in and ignited, then the engine should run under its own power. An alternative method of starting an engine is to use a blast of compressed air from somewhere, such as a reservoir bottle, a ground power unit, the APU compressor, or one of the other engines which is already running.

High-pressure air bled from the engine compressors is used mainly for cabin pressurisation, and when conditions require it, for de-icing. Compressed air is hot, as you will know if you have ever pumped a bicycle tyre by hand, so to prevent ice forming on the wings, tail and engine intakes, compressed air is piped along the leading edges of all these parts. More of this 'bleed air' is fed through the flight deck, passenger cabin and baggage holds at a carefully controlled pressure. First it must be cooled down, using cold 'ram air' collected from outside the aircraft by means of scoops, then passed through an air-conditioning unit to remove

The directional signals from the localiser transmitter of the Instrument Landing System (shown above) help the crew of a Tristar find their way to the runway (*below, a British Airways photograph*).

*Opposite* Easily the neatest of small jetliners, a Fokker F-28 Fellowship lands in a slight crosswind (*Fokker B.V.*).

excess moisture. The result is a warm, dry atmosphere inside the aircraft, in which passengers can sit in shirt-sleeved comfort.

The engines also provide electric power, driving one or more alternators connected to the high-speed gearbox. Important systems are duplicated, or even triplicated, and if necessary, 28v DC batteries can be used to power the essential services.

Complex hydraulic systems operate the flight controls, the undercarriage and its doors, flaps, slats, brakes, speedbrakes, thrust reversers, etc. There are usually at least two independent systems, each with a pump per engine working at 3000psi (9000psi in the bigger jets). Should one system fail, the others can cope, and even if there is complete hydraulic failure, back-up systems can be used; even the good old human muscle-power in an emergency.

In order that jetliners can land and take off using runways of reasonable length, increasing effort in recent years has gone into the design of 'high-lift devices', that is flaps and slats, to improve the lifting ability of the wing at low speeds. Early flap systems were simple hinges at the back of the wing. When the flap was down, it increased the suction over the top of the wing. Modern flap systems first extend backwards to increase the wing area, then hinge downwards; these are called Fowler flaps. The lift of a Fowler flap can be increased still further by dividing it into smaller sections, with aerodynamic slots in between. These slots suck air at high speed to delay stalling. The Fowler flaps fitted to the Boeing 737 and 747 are triple-slotted, and when these complicated systems begin to extend as the plane comes in to land, passengers at the rear of the aircraft sometimes fear that the wing is falling apart! Reliable mechanical devices are needed to operate these multi-slotted flaps and their counterparts on the front edge of the wing, the slats and Krüger flaps. Slats extend forwards and

downwards, producing a powerful aerodynamic slot. Krüger flaps have no slot; they hinge downwards and forwards from the undersurface of the wing.

Aircraft also have a water supply. Water from washbasins can be drained off into the airstream through an airlock (with a heated duct to prevent freezing). However, so much water is required to flush the toilets that it has to be recycled for use again and again, after it has been filtered, disinfected and perfumed. Between flights a Water Service truck comes and empties the loos.

On and around the flight deck is the place one finds a jetliner's eyes, ears and brains. To a layman, the complexity of controls, instruments, switches, warning lights, radios and black boxes is baffling, but there is a standard layout which makes most jetliner flight decks broadly similar. The controls are fully powered, but they have the same 'feel' as those of a lightplane. The main instruments are just where the lightplane pilot would expect to find them, but they display a lot of additional information gleaned from other instruments and systems, so that during a difficult landing approach in bad weather, for example, all that the pilot needs to know is displayed directly in front of him.

A jetliner has up to a dozen or more radio devices by which it communicates and navigates, each with its own aerial housed in, or protruding from, some part of the aircraft's structure. There will be long wires for short-wave radio, short spikes and ramshorns for VHF and for the VOR/ILS navigation and landing systems, towel rails for the direction finders, and small fins for DME and ATC radar. In order to keep an eye out ahead for thunderstorms, the plastic nosecone houses a search radar, which will also pick out another aircraft or the shape of a coastline.

At one time all these gadgets were separate systems which could be fitted to an aircraft and each left to get on with its own job. Not

so any more. This is the age of the micro-chip, of information technology and of integrated flight systems. The different black boxes are wired into one another, and every instrument seems to want to know what its neighbour is thinking and doing. Then they vie with each other to supply this information to the automatic pilot, and sometimes the human pilot too. Just who or what *does* fly the plane?

For many decades now, instruments based on gyroscopes have made it possible for pilots to fly a compass course, straight and level, at night or in cloud. The next development was to fit servo-mechanisms to enable these same gyroscopes to give their instructions to an automatic pilot, which could then be made to fly a chosen course straight and level. Increasingly sophisticated autopilots soon followed. Today, if a pilot wants to change course, he need not touch the rudder pedals. He simply dials a new compass heading, or the course to the next radio beacon, into the autopilot. He now has a choice between letting the autopilot turn the plane smoothly onto its new course, and using his own hands and feet to make the same turn, guided by the crossed wires of the flight director instrument placed conveniently just in front of him.

The very precise radio beams of the Instrument Landing System (ILS), which are transmitted from the ground at most airports, will show up on a pilot's instruments as an arrangement of pointers guiding him down towards the runway at an angle of 3 degrees by instructing him when to fly left or right, up or down. Alternatively by feeding the signals into the autopilot, and with a radio altimeter measuring the decreasing height above the ground, a fully automatic 'hands-off' landing is possible. The plane can find its own way down the ILS beams as far as the runway, flattening out just before a perfect touchdown.

Equally sophisticated are the navigating systems. Some use gyroscopes to sense changes in speed and direction and compute these to give a readout of the plane's geographical position. Errors of the order of one mile in 500 must be allowed for, but they are no problem if there are radio beacons within range; the computer uses these to correct errors in its own calculations and to present the autopilot with updated instructions!

It begins to look as though the human pilot is superfluous, but this of course is far from true. He is the one who is ultimately responsible for ensuring that the whole set-up works safely and efficiently. If problems arise, it's no use blaming a machine!

# Airbus and After

The big aerospace success of recent years has been that of the Airbus, a 300-seat wide-bodied jetliner designed for short-to-medium length routes and powered by two large turbofans, built by a European consortium (which includes British Aerospace) and currently being turned out at a rate of eight per month. At present the Airbus A300 and its smaller sister the A310 are outselling Boeing in the wide-body market.

When the big, new turbofan engines began to appear in the mid-1960s, the Americans concentrated on the medium-to-long range market, thinking that this would be most profitable. So they built the Boeing 747, the DC-10 and the Tristar, using three or four big engines. They neglected to produce a twin-engined wide-body designed for short-to-medium range routes, and a number of British and European plane-makers began to have joint talks about filling this gap. After the usual political wranglings about who does what, who supplies the engines and who pays the bills, a basic design was agreed upon, and an international consortium, Airbus Industrie, was formed to co-ordinate design, production and marketing. The first Airbus A300 took to the skies above Toulouse on 28 October 1972, and the first production models, the A300B2, entered passenger service with Air France and Lufthansa in 1974. At the time, however, other customers seemed scarce.

It was the oil crisis of 1973–4 which sparked off Airbus sales. Suddenly the cost of fuel had become very important and the airlines were beginning to think of buying aircraft which were more fuel-efficient. The A300s, which could carry 300 passengers using only two of the big, new, high-by-pass turbofans, and with a very advanced wing, were proving to be very economical to operate compared with older designs such as the Boeing 727. Orders for the Airbus started to pour in.

It is worth listing the technical reasons behind the Airbus A300's outstanding fuel economy. First the engines themselves – they may not be Rolls Royces, but they come very close: General Electric CF-6-50s, built under licence in France and Germany. Secondly there are only two of them and they are cheaper to run and maintain than three engines. If the A300 had been designed for long-range routes, it would need to carry more fuel, would need a third engine, more sweepback, more wing and tail area, and would weigh 20 tonnes more, *not* counting the weight of the extra engine and fuel. Thirdly, the wings themselves, designed in Britain using the latest aerofoil section. This works well at high Mach numbers with only 28 degrees sweepback, which is much less than that of its rivals. This powerful wing can lift the Airbus quickly to its most economical cruising altitude, yet lose height and speed easily without stomping on the speedbrakes. In order to operate from short runways, the wing has all the latest high-lift devices, such as long-span tabbed Fowler flaps and full-

*Above* Airbus A300s move along the assembly line at the Aerospatiale factory at St Martin, near Toulouse (*Airbus Industrie*).

*Right* Near-completed A300s park nose in to the 'Abreuvoir' (cattle-trough) for the final pre-flight preparations (*Airbus Industrie*).

*Opposite* A newly completed Airbus A300 leaves Toulouse on delivery to the Chilean airline Cruzeiro do Sul (*Airbus Industrie*).

span slats. On the Airbus A300B4 the efficiency of the slats has been improved still further. Between the inboard end of the slat and the fuselage there is now a small Krüger flap, and at the inboard end of this a tiny vane swings out from the fuselage to fill the triangular notch which remains.

In fact the basic design of the Airbus is so straightforward, that it can be modified easily to incorporate even newer developments as they occur, resulting in further improvements in performance and fuel-efficiency. This development process was envisaged from the beginning, and is now well under way.

The early production Airbuses were the A300B2s, with a maximum take-off weight of 142 tonnes, and a range of 2000 miles. This is still available as the short-range version, but it has now been joined in service by the A300B4 which has a range of over 3000 miles and an increased take-off weight to allow for the extra fuel.

The A300B4-100 and the even heavier longer-range A300B4-200 (the version operated by Laker Airways) are still the same overall size as the original B2, and although a slightly stretched version, the A300-600, is planned for service in 1984, most Airbus development effort is now concentrated on two *smaller* planes, the 200-seat wide-bodied A310 and the 160-seat A320. The A310 uses the same fuselage cross-section as the A300, but is some $6\frac{1}{2}$ metres shorter, with a redesigned wing and less powerful engines. The new wing of the A310 is even more advanced than that of the A300. The double-curved wing-skin panels are bent into shape by 'shot blasting' and the result will be the most efficient wing in the sky when the A310 flies in 1982. The A320, still a design study, will be the first narrow-bodied Airbus, powered by two fuel-efficient turbofans of around 11 tonnes thrust. All the new designs, beginning with the A310, are being offered

*Opposite* On later versions of the A300 Airbus, the efficiency of the full-span leading-edge slat has been considerably improved by fitting a small Krüger flap at the inboard end. The remaining triangular notch is closed by means of a small device which swings out from the fuselage. *Below* The arrangement with the Krüger flap partly extended (*Airbus Industrie*).

Fuel-saving ideas from McDonnell-Douglas.

*Above* Many Series 60 DC-8s are being refitted with quieter, more fuel-efficient CFM-56 turbofans. This has now become a DC-8-71 (*McDonnell-Douglas*).
*Below* A DC-10-10 with small winglets to reduce wingtip vortex drag (*McDonnell-Douglas*).

Will the jetliners of the nineties be almost indistinguishable?

*Above* Airbus A310, 200-seat twin aisle (*British Caledonian Airways*).

*Right* Airbus A320, 160-seat single-aisle (*Airbus Industrie*).

*Above* Boeing 767,
250-seat twin-aisle
(*Boeing*).

*Left* Boeing 757 200-
seat single-aisle
(*Boeing*).

A new jetliner especially designed for the short-haul trade, the BAE 146 (*British Aerospace*).

with a new electronic flight deck in which conventional instruments are replaced by video displays.

Airbus is a consortium, and the various parts of the aircraft were built all over Europe, and transported fully wired and plumbed in a Super Guppy freighter to the final assembly line in the Aerospatiale factory at Toulouse. The wings come from Chester, the fuselage sections from Germany, and the tailplane from Spain. At Toulouse the aircraft takes shape, is painted, and makes its first flight. It goes to Hamburg for interior finishing before returning to Toulouse for delivery to the customer airline. The system clearly works, and very efficiently, but the Airbus is not just a French aeroplane; it is a European joint effort.

Boeing is having to look to its laurels. The new Boeing 767 wide-body is a direct competitor for the A310, the narrow-body Boeing 757 will be slightly smaller, and McDonnell-Douglas are joining forces with Fokker to build the MDF-100, a rival for the A320. Planespotters of the future will have a hard task; all these new designs look remarkably alike.

But other planemakers will also be busy, even in what will surely be continuing hard times for civil aviation. A market is opening up for jetliners specially designed for short-haul operations, such as the Fokker F-28 Fellowship and the new British Aerospace 146. The small commuter airliners who fly the short-haul routes find that they can no longer remain competitive using old, second-hand turboprop aircraft, and in developing countries there is a similar demand for aircraft which are economical to operate, which don't need concrete runways, and which are easy to service. Both types of operation require basically the same virtues. Economy comes first. A short-haul jetliner should be cheap to fly and to maintain, and should be able to get up to an economical cruising altitude even on a flight as short as 150 miles. This means the kind of agility which can get in and out of 'tight' airfields; a steep climb and descent and slow landing and take-off speeds. After economy and agility comes ruggedness. A short-haul jetliner will have a hard working life, landing and taking off many times a day, sometimes without refuelling, and sometimes on the roughest of runways. For commuter use, reliability and punctuality are very important, and the plane must be quiet enough not to make enemies of the local townspeople.

Fokker got in first with their beautiful little F-28 Fellowship, which first flew in 1969. On the surface it looks like a BAC 1-11 or a DC-9 with its two rear-mounted engines and T-tail. Power is provided by two Rolls Royce RB-183 turbofans, developed from the Spey, but smaller, quieter and easier to maintain. Its powerful wings give the F-28 the low take-off and landing speeds and the steep climb necessary to make a success of short-haul flying, and getting down and stopping in a hurry is helped by the tail-mounted speedbrake and large wing-spoilers. Thrust reversers are unnecessary. Nearly 200 Fokker F-28s have been sold, particularly in the developing regions of the world.

The British Aerospace 146 first flew on 3 September 1981 and is even more closely tailored to the needs of short-haul flying.

Cutaway diagram of the Rolls Royce RB-211-535 (*Rolls Royce Limited*).

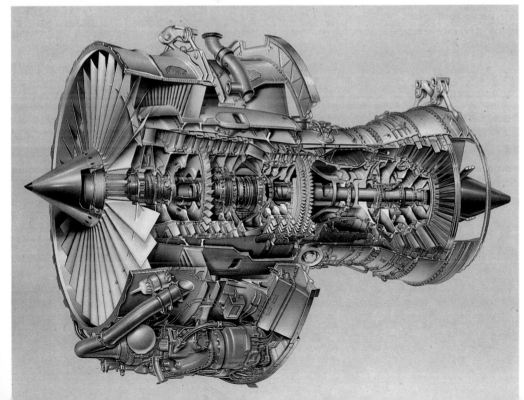

With four engines rather than two, it must immediately appear more expensive both to buy and to maintain, but these are new-technology Avco Lycoming ALF-502 turbofans, very fuel-efficient, quiet and designed for easy maintenance. With four engines, the 146 can climb away safely, even if one engine should fail on take-off, and to simplify maintenance it can ferry a dead engine back to its home base. The fuselage-mounted undercarriage is very rugged, enabling the 146 to do four quick turnrounds without refuelling. Powerful wings give a steep climb and descent, and for short hops, the modest cruising speed of Mach 0.7 is no disadvantage. Slinging the four engines on longish pylons beneath the high wing means that the flaps are long and efficient, unbroken by cutouts for the jet exhaust.

When one sees jetliners such as the Fokker Fellowship and the BAe 146 operating regular no-fuss schedules out of small-town airfields, or in some cases dried-up river beds or forest clearings, their indigenous but highly trained crews fully conversant with the job of running an airline, it is difficult to resist the conclusion that air travel is here to stay. Flying is now for everyone, not just a privileged minority, and the jetliner is a con-

*Top, centre, left and above* A modern Flying Dutchman, the go-anywhere Fokker F-28 Fellowship (*Fokker B.V.*).

venience like roads and railways but probably cheaper. The old political debates which have surrounded civil aviation since it began in 1919, that is whether or not those who can afford to fly should subsidise those who cannot, or vice-versa, are now largely irrelevant. Perhaps we have achieved something by uniting our diverse world in a common technical enterprise and adventure.

*Below* Winter scene at Bromma, Sweden (*Fokker B.V.*).

# Index